THE
GOLFER'S GUIDE TO
WORLD HISTORY

AMERICAN GOLFIC
after Grant Wood
I suppose he'd be called Grant Metal these days

THE GOLFER'S GUIDE TO WORLD HISTORY

65 Golfing Cartoons
by
MARTYN TURNER

Irish Life & Permanent plc

THE
BLACKSTAFF
PRESS
BELFAST

Thanks to Michael and Pat and the *Irish Times*
generally for aid, succour and indulgence.

Thanks also to Lucy, Cullum and Jean for other
help, and to my golfing co-conspirators for
pretending to appreciate the jokes when I tried
them out on the first tee.

Martyn Turner's political cartoons can be seen
in the *Irish Times* and at
www.ireland.com/cartoons/turner

First published in 1999 by
The Blackstaff Press Limited
Blackstaff House, Wildflower Way, Apollo Road
Belfast BT12 6TA, Northern Ireland

© Martyn Turner, 1999
All rights reserved

Martyn Turner has asserted his right under the
Copyright, Designs and Patents Act 1988 to be identified
as the author of this work.

Designed by Della Varilly Design

Printed in Ireland by Betaprint

A CIP catalogue record for this book
is available from the British Library

ISBN 0-85640-663-5

'History is bunk'

HENRY FORD
(1863–1947)

'History is bunkers'

MARTYN TURNER
(1948 – still feeling OK, generally, thanks very much)

Introduction

Being a political cartoonist it is necessary to stay on the ball, stay abreast of events, keep one's finger on the pulse, know where it's at (and who is at it), constantly test the water of public opinion, and avoid clichés wherever possible. So when the lady whom I call, in my weaker, less humble moments, 'my publisher' rang and asked what I wanted to do this year I was immediately able to say: 'What the world really needs at the moment is another golf book.'

She seemed amazed. After all there are at least 2 million different golf books already in circulation. They cut down forests to print the things. They then build another championship golf course on the land the trees vacated. (They never build a run-of-the-mill golf course, you notice, always a championship one.) It is nature's way of turning the entire planet into one vast golf course. This is the point of my book. Golf is what nature used to be. It is the philosophy of life. It has been the philosophy of history as you will tenuously see if you get further into this book than the introduction. The rules of golf are the rules of existence. The etiquette of golf is what the United Nations charter should be. The camaraderie of golf is a blueprint for a future where all men and women live in peace and harmony and wear brightly coloured clothes. And if you believe that . . .

I have been playing golf since I was seven years old. The part of London where I grew up was pleasant inasmuch as it was where suburbia collided with Epping Forest and by royal decree could go no further. At that point of collision was a nine-hole golf course. It was built on public land. Cows and bulls had the right to graze on it and we, the members, had to wear red to warn the hiking, dog-walking, picnicking and fornicating public of our presence. It was a quiet golf course – I don't think such things exist now. Me and my mate Dave had the place pretty much to ourselves for the whole of every summer. Round and round and round we went. It got so boring we invented new ways to play. We'd play the course backwards. We'd play the holes backwards. We would take putters off the tee and putt with a driver. At lunchtimes we would play round with two postmen, a father and son, who, in order to get round in the time allotted, putted with their mail bags still on their backs and ate their lunch walking down the fairways. On reflection, it was a great way to grow up. When I was sixteen I could break eighty with some sort of regularity. It was obvious that it was only a matter of time before I won the British Open. Dave went off to be a mechanic in the RAF, never to be heard of (by me) again. So I hung around the golf club on my own. In between golf games I would get under the feet of the overworked professional at our club. He was, I think, also the greenkeeper and the steward. I would be left in charge of selling the Warwicks and the Spitfires and, if a rich geezer called in, the Dunlop 65s when he was off on his other duties. Our professional was an ex-member who hadn't been doing a lot at the time the club thought it might like a professional, so they offered him a job. He was, without doubt one of the best players at the club. He was the course record holder. He had no idea why or how he was a good player, nor why he was the course record holder. He had a swing that made John Daly's look a little on the short side, which proved to be a problem when it came to teaching. The very strength of his own game – 'well I just hit it' – doesn't go very far in imparting knowledge when it comes to giving lessons. But it remains a fine piece of technical advice.

He found it difficult to tell pupils anything other than just 'hit it'. He agreed to teach a bunch of students from London University and when they arrived *en masse* one Wednesday afternoon he panicked, made an excuse and left and told me to go and teach them. Twenty students, none of whom had been on a golf course before, all strung out across the width of the first fairway being told what to do by me – Mr Spotty Gangly Youth. It was then I decided that telling other people, older and maybe wiser, what to do was what I enjoyed best.

At the end of the summer the professional offered me a job doing what I had been doing for free but now getting paid for it. Selling golf balls, giving lessons, fixing clubs, playing golf. This seemed a better proposition than a few more horrendous years at school. So I accepted the job. I worked on Saturday, I worked on Sunday, and then on Monday – the first day of term – I dressed for work again.

'Where are you going dressed like that?' my mother said.

'I've left school,' I said. 'I've got a job at the golf club.'

My mother LOOKED AT ME. Before the advent of nuclear weapons my mother looking in an easterly direction was all that kept the communist hordes at bay. She turned her look volume control all the way up to eleven. She rarely went above seven when keeping Kruschev at bay.

I went upstairs and put my school uniform on.

The rest is history – well, my history. Two more years at school. A bit of a year off. Four years at Queen's University Belfast playing at Royal County Down for seven and sixpence and then to the *Irish Times,* getting paid to tell politicians and other sundry sorts where they are going wrong, what they ought to do. It's what I enjoy doing best.

I was caddying for a friend recently in a senior cup match. His opponent's caddy was an ex-professional, reinstated as an amateur.

'I was a professional once, too,' I said as we were introduced. (I say this to as many people as I can, as often as I can. Sad, isn't it?)

'Sixteen years I did,' he said, 'and then I just got sick of it. You?'

'Two days,' I said, 'and then my mother looked at me.'

KILDARE
SEPTEMBER 1999

THE CREATION

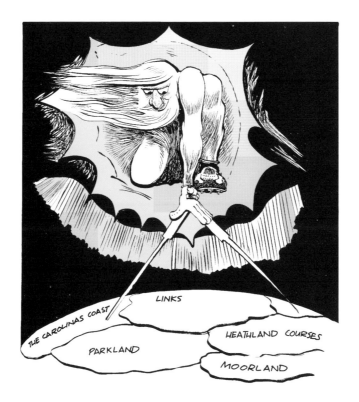

THE ROYAL AND ANCIENT OF DAYS
after William Blake

In the beginning was the Word, and the Word
was God – Golf? – something like that. The
proof (if proof is needed) that God created the
universe by hitting planets off his celestial
driving range can be seen in the phenomenon
of planetary backspin. Soft-centred and
soft-cored planets have slowed down, almost
come to a stop since the Big Bang, whereas
Planet Pinnacle is still splitting the celestial
fairway at a rapid rate of knots.

THE GARDEN OF EDEN
The Perennial Question

EVOLUTION

The Stone Age was, of course, followed by
the Iron Age, which in turn led to the
Persimmon Age which lasted from the
twelfth century until 1994, which then begat
the Metal Age (1994–98), which begat the
Ceramic Age (early 1998–summer 1998),
which begat the Titanium Age (summer
1998–summer 1999), which begat the
Trimetal Age (summer 1999 until they think
up something else for us to buy).

STONE AGE MAN DISCOVERS A NEW TOOL

The Cave Age

LONG LONG TIME AGO, BEFORE SKY SPORTS

THE PLAGUES OF THE CHILDREN OF ISRAEL, OR SOMEONE

MOSES BRINGS DOWN COMMANDMENTS 11 THROUGH 134

NOAH CLAIMS CASUAL WATER

MOSES PLAYING OUT OF A LATERAL WATER HAZARD

SOLOMON AND AN EARLY RULES COMMITTEE DECISION

DAVID FIELD TESTS AN EARLY ONE-PIECE GOLF BALL

13

NARCISSUS

SISYPHUS ATTEMPTS TO LEGALISE THE GREEK-GOD-SIZED GOLF BALL

RELIGIOUS MYTHS AND STORIES

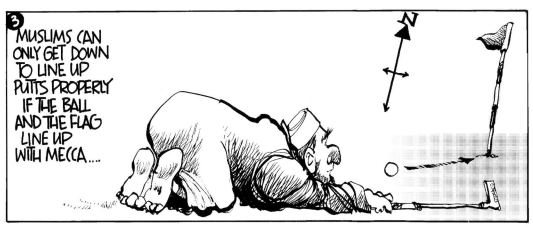

RELIGIOUS MYTHS AND STORIES

Boadicea, sometimes called Boudicca, the British warrior queen who died in AD 62, was famed for her chariot with its wheels full of knives. Believed to be the world's first greenkeeper, she is also credited with inventing the 'gutty' golf ball – made from the guts and sinews of her slain enemies. She is seen here playing the famous 'wode hole' at Royal Cromer.

BOADICEA IMPROVES HER LIE IN THE ROUGH

NG
OUT OF BOUNDS
IT IS NOT PERMITTED TO CROSS THE WALL TO RETRIEVE BALLS UNDER ANY CIRC-UMSTANCES
by order Hadrian

HADRIAN'S WALL

THE FIRST INTERNAL OUT-OF-BOUNDS FENCE

Of course these days the wall is not internal – or is, depending on your politics. The Romans were well aware of the wealth of the wind-blown, rough terrain links courses that Scotland enjoyed and also knew the Scots, consequently, had handicaps born out of those desperately difficult conditions. The wall was designed to keep the Scots away from the namby-pamby English parkland layouts where, with their handicaps, they would have cleaned up and taken all the prizes.

THE DUTCH DISCOVER GOLF . . .

. . . AND WHY IT NEVER CAUGHT ON

SCOTLAND

There's something I've always wondered. If
the Scots actually discovered golf, which is
generally accepted now, and if golf clubs
have always been bastions of conservatism
where 'correct dress will be worn at all
times', then how come we don't all play in
kilts and sporrans? Sporrans would be great
places to keep tees and pencils and ball
markers and pitch mark repairers.

COLUMBUS SETS THE PRECEDENT FOR USELESS GOLF TROPHIES . . .

. . . or as Randy Newman put it on his latest, greatest album (*Hard Love* – go! buy!):
'Great nations of Europe coming through . . .'

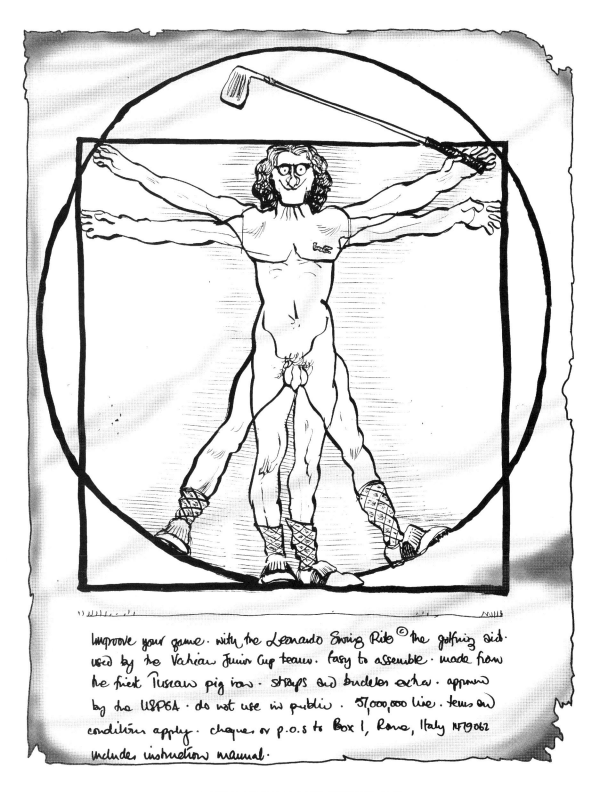

Improve your game . with the Leonardo Swing Rite © the golfing aid.
used by the Vatican Junior Cup team. Easy to assemble . made from
the finest Tuscan pig iron . straps and buckles extra . approved
by the USPGA . do not use in public . 57,000,000 lire . terms and
conditions apply . cheques or p.o.s to Box 1, Rome, Italy Nº79062
includes instruction manual .

THE FIRST GOLF-SWING AID

After discarding Catherine of Aragon, Anne
Boleyn, Jane Seymour, Anne of Cleves and
Catherine Howard, Henry VIII went searching
for another suitable wifely candidate. And if you
want to play golf you can't do any better than
pick someone called Parr (Catherine).

HENRY VIII LOOKS FOR ANOTHER MIXED FOURSOMES PARTNER

WHEN THE WORLD WAS FLAT

After discovering the round golf ball, Galileo took the next logical step and declared that the earth itself was probably round, too. This, of course, created even more consternation within the Church, which had been enthusiastically declaring the earth to be flat. Galileo made a considerable fortune by nipping over the horizon and gathering up all the balls the Church had declared 'out of bounds' – slipped off the earth altogether – and reselling them. All of these 'previously owned' balls were square, naturally, but there was still a ready market as people went on believing what the Church said about flat earths and cubic golf balls despite all evidence to the contrary. Some people still believe what the Church says even today.

GALILEO THEORISES THAT THE GOLF BALL MIGHT BE A SPHERE

THE PERSECUTION OF THE GOLF PSYCHOLOGISTS

THE INTRODUCTION OF SOFT SPIKES SPELLED THE END FOR THE INQUISITION

THE COMTE DE PANNISSEAU MAKES THE CUT

NAPOLEON RETREATS FROM MOSCOW – COURSE CLOSED

THE FIRST ATTEMPT BY A WOMAN TO JOIN A MEN'S CLUB
JEANNE D'ARC

GEORGE WASHINGTON PLAYS THE SEVENTEENTH AT SAWGRASS
after Emanuel Leutze

YOUNG GEORGE WASHINGTON

AN EARLY WOOD CUT
metals are supposedly straighter

WHILST WAITING FOR HIS TEE, JAMES WATT INVENTS THE REVETTED BUNKER

EINSTEIN'S FIRST BOOK   EINSTEIN'S SECOND BOOK

HENRY MORTON STANLEY PREPARES FOR HIS TRIP AT CARNOUSTIE

PUTTING MARX ON YOUR CARD

We recently had a guest from across the water who devoted some portion of his visit to regaling us with the wonders of Thatcherism. Despite what I see as evidence to the contrary, he assured us that a return to primitive selfish economics was doing Britain a power of good.

'Hard work,' he said, 'bicycle riding in search of same, et cetera, never did any harm. People are getting away with too much. They're being mollycoddled.'

Later in the week we went to play golf. We reached the first green, a par five. I was twelve feet away after three shots. He was on the edge of the green after four.

'How many shots are you giving me?' he said.

'Shots!' I said. 'Shots! I thought you were a Thatcherite?'

'What do you mean?' he said.

'Well,' I expounded, 'as I understand it, you are a Thatcherite. You believe in standing-on-your-own-two-feetedness. I happen to be a better golfer than you. My handicap, at the last count, was twenty-one shots better than yours . . . I wasn't born with a low handicap. It was achieved by the sweat of my brow. I spent many, many days as a teenager slaving away on a golf course when I could have been going to school, learning how to be a financier or playing snooker. I have calluses on my hands from the thousands of shots I hit on the practice ground. If I understand your present philosophy right, you believe that it is open to everyone to play off single figures. It only takes application, good old-fashioned hard work. If I start giving you shots it would only encourage you in your slothfulness. Where would the incentive be to better yourself? Why should I give you a handout of shots just because you happen to be, in the economics of golf, worse off than myself. I wouldn't insult your dignity by feather-bedding you.'

He tried to speak but I was in full flow now.

'You have opened my eyes,' I said. 'I now see the handicapping system for what it is. A socialist conspiracy intent on making us all equal. Merit on the golf course achieves no reward. It seems to me that the handicapping section of the Golfing Union of Ireland must be some sort of front for Moscow. They must be, at the very least, members of the Workers' Party or the Emmet Stagg wing of the Labour Party. I thank you. After thirty years I at last realise that golf is a game played by capitalists but organised by communists. I will have a new respect for those people in blazers with badges that run the whole show.'

'Is that a no?' he asked. 'Am I not getting any shots?'

'It's up to you,' I said. 'We can play it your way – survival of the fittest. Or we can play according to the true revolutionary Marxist principles of the game and I will support you, my weaker comrade. And anyway, I suppose I should be kind to my father.'

On the second tee some ladies had been waiting patiently. Being mere women and seeing *men* approaching, they were waiting to let us through. The revolution has a way to go yet, comrade golfers.

Irish Times, July 1990

KARL MARX GETS HIS BIG IDEA

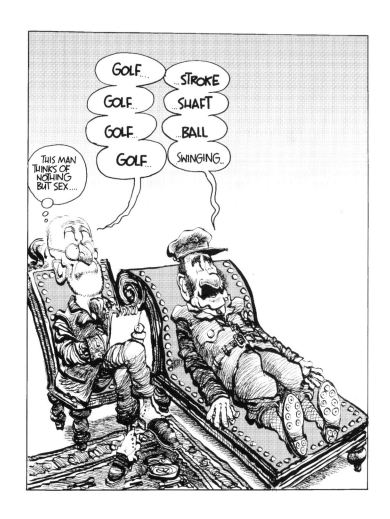

FREUD GETS HIS BIG IDEA

**CHARLES STEWART PARNELL AND KITTY O'SHEA
BEFORE PLAYING AROUND WITH EACH OTHER**

WORLD WAR ONE – GROUND UNDER REPAIR

**NEVILLE CHAMBERLAIN RETURNS FROM MUNICH
WITH AN INCORRECTLY MARKED SCORECARD**

HITLER AND GOEBBELS FAIL THE MEDICAL FOR A FOURBALL COMPETITION

RODIN'S *THE PUTTER*

**TENZING ATTENDS THE FLAG AS EDMUND HILLARY COMPLETES THE
UPHILL EIGHTEENTH AT EVEREST, OR VICE VERSA**

WHERE BEATNIKS GOT THE IDEA TO BECOME HIPPIES

HALLOWE'EN AFTER BROOMSTICK PUTTERS

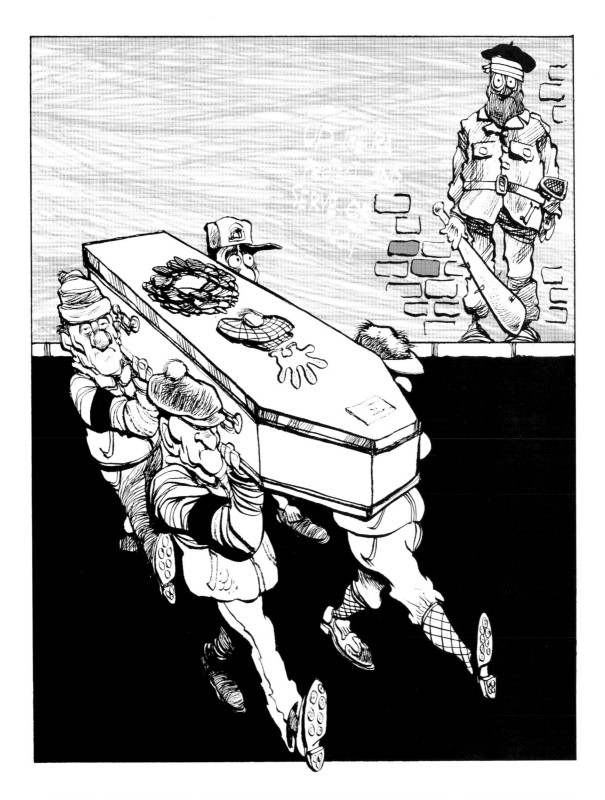

THE BEGINNER WHO MISUNDERSTOOD THE TERM 'HIT A PROVISIONAL'

BILL CLINTON – WHERE GOLF AND POLITICS MEET

Crib Sheet

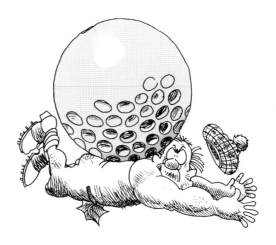

Since my recall of bits of history are probably different from everyone else's bits of history recalled, here are a few pointers to the more obscure references.

page 15
Sisyphus was the king of Corinth, allegedly punished for his misdeeds by eternally being obliged to push a large stone up a hill.

page 40
This is a bastardised version of a famous American painting called
Washington Crossing the Delaware. The seventeenth at Sawgrass is an island green where a million golf balls a year are deposited in the surrounding lake.

page 43
James Watt invented the steam engine after watching a kettle boil.

page 49 (for those outside Ireland)
Famous political scandal and divorce case.

page 50
The original Big Bertha was a huge German gun used to bombard Paris in World War One.

page 55 (for those outside Britain and Ireland)
The words of 'Colonel Bogey', a wartime song, suggested that Hitler and Goebbels were testicularly challenged.